W9-CMD-617

DR. J. BRONOWSKI is the distinguished author of such noted adult books as SCIENCE AND HUMAN VALUES and THE WESTERN INTELLECTUAL TRADITION. Educated at Cambridge University in England, Dr. Bronowski has been a Head of Projects for UNESCO, a Carnegie Visiting Professor at the Massachusetts Institute of Technology, and is a Foreign Honorary Member of the American Academy of Arts and Sciences. At present he is engaged in research at the Salk Institute for Biological Studies, in California.

MILLICENT E. SELSAM, a native New Yorker, majored in biology at Brooklyn College, took her M.A. in botany at Columbia University, and has taught biology on both the high school and college levels. Her writing has received wide acclaim for its scientific accuracy and simple presentation. Mrs. Selsam is a member of the Board of Directors of the American Nature Study Society and a Fellow of the American Association for the Advancement of Science.

WEIMER PURSELL studied at the Art Institute and the New Bauhaus School of Design in Chicago. Except for five years of college teaching, his whole career has been devoted to free-lance work in design and illustration.

BIOGRAPHY OF AN ATOM

ILLUSTRATED WITH PICTURES BY **WEIMER PURSELL**

and with photographs

BIOGRAPHY
OF AN ATOM

by

J. BRONOWSKI and

MILLICENT E. SELSAM

DISCARD

HARPER & ROW, Publishers
New York, Evanston, and London

17520

Hiram Halle Memorial Library
Pound Ridge, New York

J
541.2
B

This book is based on an article which originally appeared in The New York Times.

BIOGRAPHY OF AN ATOM

Copyright © 1963 by J. Bronowski
Copyright © 1965 by J. Bronowski and Millicent E. Selsam

Printed in the United States of America. All rights reserved. No part of this book may be used or reproduced in any manner whatsoever without written permission except in the case of brief quotations embodied in critical articles and reviews. For information address Harper & Row, Publishers, Incorporated, 49 East 33rd Street, New York 16, N. Y.

Library of Congress Catalog Card Number: 64-19708

BIOGRAPHY OF AN ATOM

THIS IS THE BIOGRAPHY OF A SINGLE ATOM—what it is like, where it came from, and its place in the world. There are about one hundred different kinds of atoms, but this story will be about an atom of carbon because carbon is found in every living cell, and its atoms therefore enter into your life and mine.

What does an atom look like? Nobody knows. It is too small to be seen. How do we know, then, that there are such things as atoms?

The reason is as plain today as it was to the Greeks who first thought of it. Suppose you take some iron powder and pick it apart into its tiniest particles. Each particle is still iron and nothing else. You could shatter the little dust particles of iron into smaller parts. The process of breaking can go on and on, but it cannot go on forever. There must be a smallest unit of iron beyond which we cannot go if we want still to have iron.

This is the picture of matter which we have had since the time of the ancient Greeks. A substance is made up of tiny pieces, each of them indivisible, each alike, and each characteristic of that substance and not something else. The Greeks called these pieces *atomos,* which means "that which cannot be divided." From this Greek word has come our modern word *atom*.

The Greeks only speculated about these things. It was not until the sixteenth century that experimental chemistry began, and it took three centuries more for scientists to find out what things are made of.

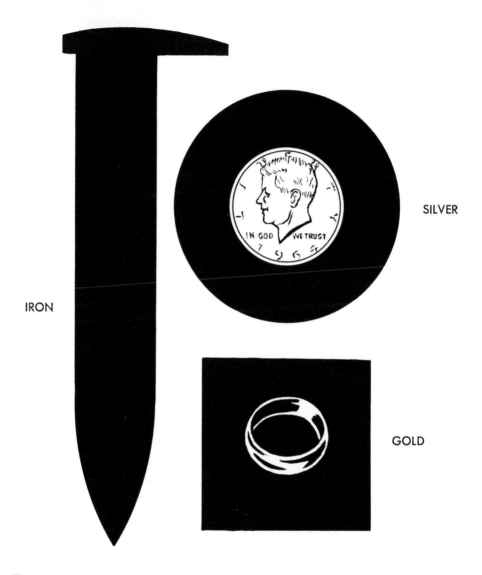

IRON

SILVER

GOLD

Experiment showed that everything in the world—rocks, water, diamonds, bones, leaves—is made up either of substances called *elements*, which cannot be broken down into simpler substances, or of *compounds*, which are combinations of elements.

We use the word atom for the smallest unit of an element, such as iron, carbon, oxygen, silver, or gold.

10

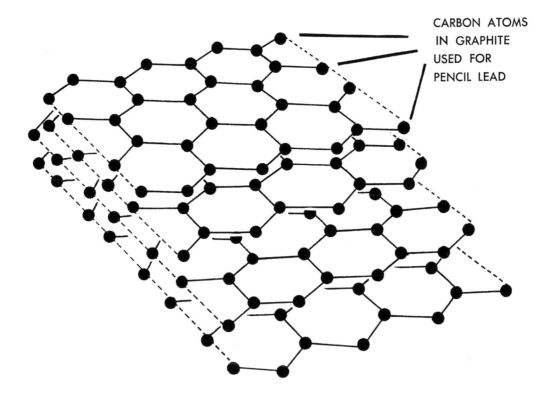

CARBON ATOMS
IN GRAPHITE
USED FOR
PENCIL LEAD

Every atom in a piece of carbon is a carbon atom. Every atom in a piece of iron is an iron atom.

The atoms of one element are different from those of another. There are therefore as many kinds of atoms as there are elements —about one hundred in all. But although there are only one hundred elements in the world, their atoms combine with others in so many different ways that they make up the million and a half different chemical compounds in the world today. We use the word *molecule* for the smallest part of a compound that is characteristic of that compound and nothing else. Each molecule is made up of a number of atoms.

2 Atoms of Hydrogen Plus 1 Atom of Oxygen = 1 Molecule of Water

1 Atom of Carbon Plus 1 Atom of Oxygen = 1 Molecule of
Carbon Monoxide
(a poisonous gas)

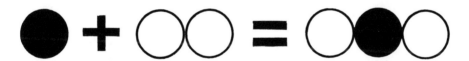

1 Atom of Carbon Plus 2 Atoms of Oxygen = 1 Molecule of
Carbon Dioxide
(a gas common to
the atmosphere)

1 Atom of Sodium Plus I Atom of Chlorine = 1 Molecule of Salt

Because experimental work has revealed the nature of the atom, it is possible to draw a diagram that is the nearest thing we can have to a picture of an atom.

Every atom has the same basic structure and is put together from the same smaller parts. Of these, three kinds of electrical particles are the most important: *protons,* which have a positive electric charge; *neutrons,* which have no electric charge; and *electrons,* which have a negative electric charge.

PROTON   NEUTRON   ELECTRON

The proton and the neutron are heavy particles. Each is almost two thousand times as heavy as an electron. And the electron is so light that it really seems to be nothing but a tiny charge of negative electricity.

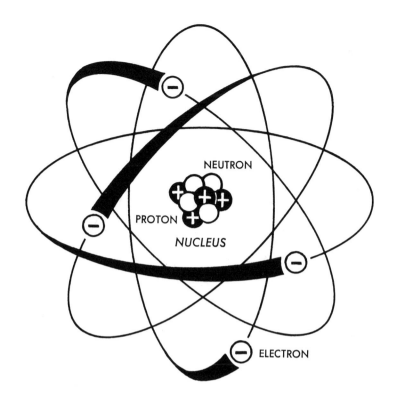

The heavy particles, the protons and the neutrons, are tightly bound together in the center of the atom, called the *nucleus*. Far away from this center are the light electrons. They are in constant movement, circling the nucleus much as planets circle the sun. But because their orbits are less exact, they form a kind of spinning cloud or shell.

The electrons may be lost and recovered. But even if they wander off, the atom will remain essentially the same. For the solid substance and anchor of every atom is its heavy nucleus. The nucleus has a positive electric charge because of its positively charged protons, and these attract an equal number of negatively charged electrons that circle around it. So there is no tendency for the whole atom to fly apart.

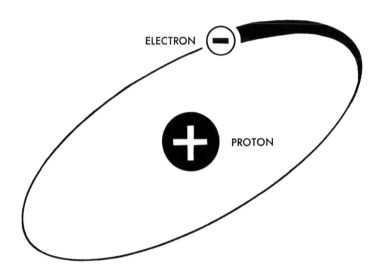

All atoms have the same fundamental particles, but they differ from one another in the number of protons and neutrons in the nucleus. In particular, each different kind of atom has a characteristic number of protons. Every atom in the gas called hydrogen has one proton.

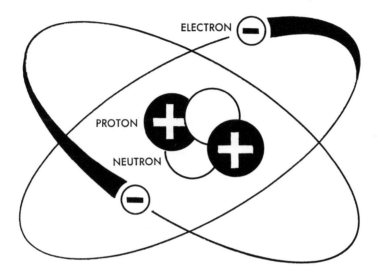

The nucleus of the gas called helium has two protons and usually two neutrons, and so on up the ladder of nature's one hundred kinds of atoms.

Each additional proton in the nucleus produces another kind of atom.

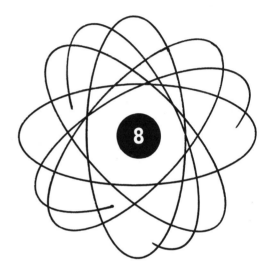

OXYGEN HAS 8 PROTONS

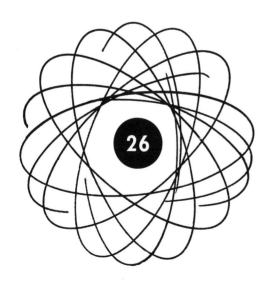

IRON HAS 26 PROTONS

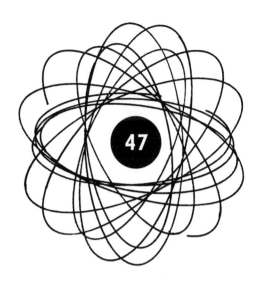

SILVER HAS 47 PROTONS

GOLD HAS 79 PROTONS

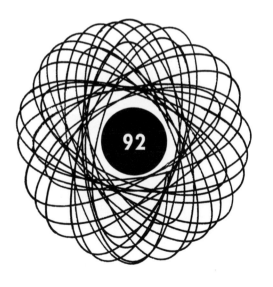

URANIUM HAS 92 PROTONS

The lightest atoms have the smallest number of protons, and the heaviest atoms have the largest number.

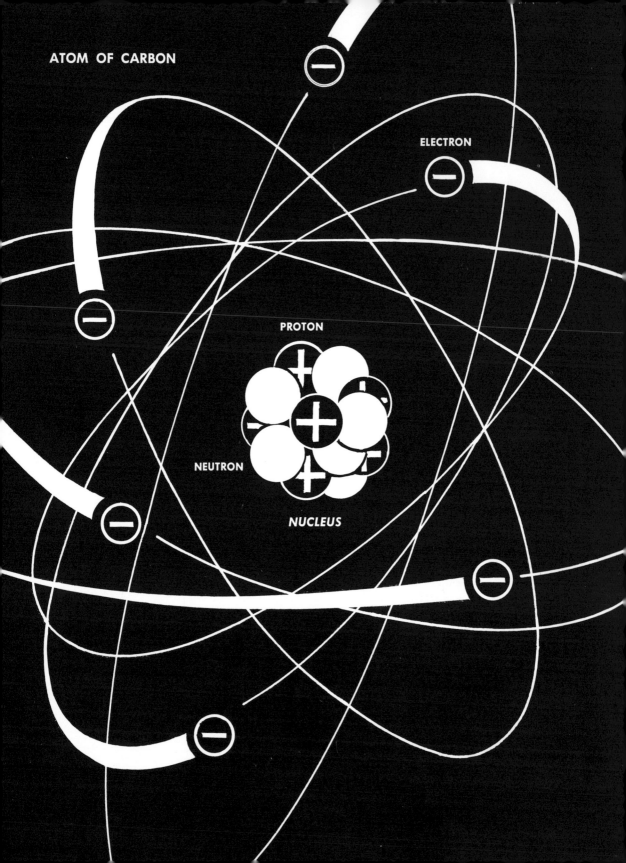

The nucleus of the carbon atom comes sixth on this ladder. It has six protons and usually six neutrons. Around the nucleus of the carbon atom six electrons circle and balance the electric charges of the six protons.

Which units are essential if the atom is to be carbon? Must it have all six electrons? No. Some of the electrons may wander off. The tremendous heat in a star can strip away all the electrons, and yet the nucleus will still remain carbon. Then must there be exactly six neutrons in the nucleus? No. There are variants, or *isotopes,* of carbon which contain one or two additional neutrons. But all isotopes of carbon have the same number of protons.

So the character of carbon lies in one number only: To be carbon an atom must have *six protons* in its nucleus, neither more nor less. This is the important number.

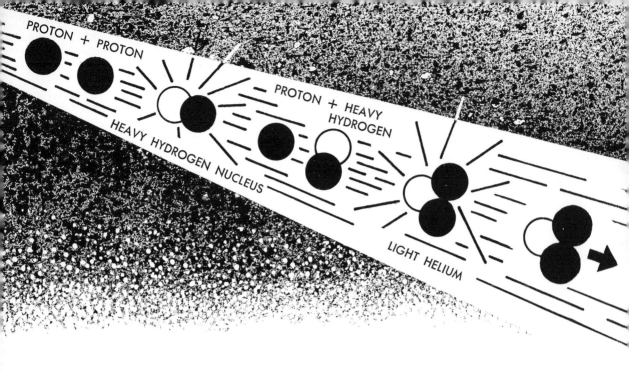

The atom of carbon has a remarkable history. It came on a long journey from the infinite spaces to the earth.

The birth began in a young star. A young star is a mass of hydrogen nuclei. Because the star is hot (about thirteen million degrees at the center), the nuclei cannot hold on to their electrons. The electrons wander around. The nuclei of hydrogen —that is, the protons—are moving about very fast too. From time to time one proton runs headlong into another. When this happens, one of the protons loses its electric charge and changes into a neutron. The pair then cling together as a single nucleus of heavy hydrogen. This nucleus will in time capture another proton. Now there is a nucleus with two protons and one neutron, called light helium. When two of these nuclei smash into each other, two protons are expelled in the process. This creates a nucleus of helium with two protons and two neutrons.

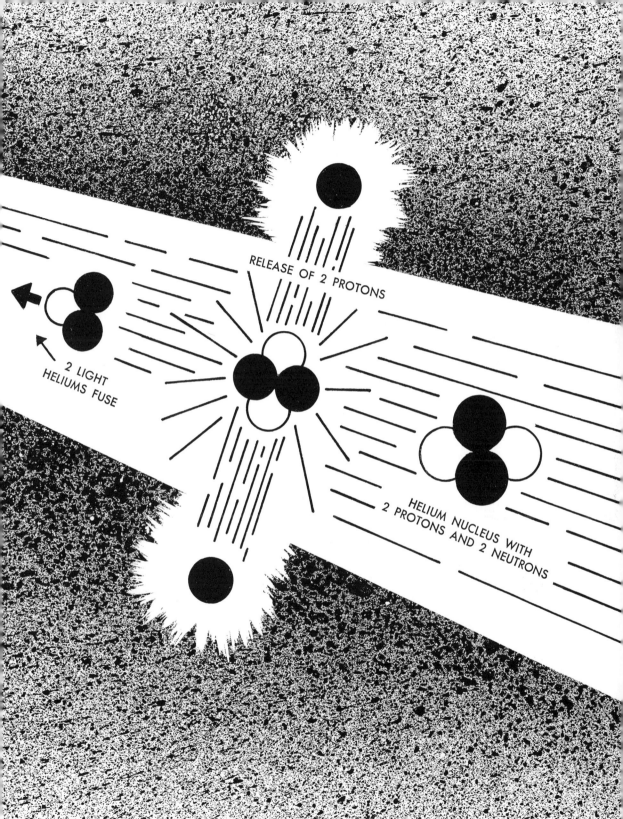

RELEASE OF 2 PROTONS

2 LIGHT
HELIUMS FUSE

HELIUM NUCLEUS WITH
2 PROTONS AND 2 NEUTRONS

This is the fundamental process of *fusion* by which the primitive hydrogen of the universe is built up into a new basic material, helium. In this process, energy is given off in the form of heat and light that make the stars shine. It is the first stage in the birth of the heavier atoms.

After billions of years, the star, now no longer young, has a central core of almost pure helium. The helium nuclei begin to run into one another headlong. Every so often two helium nuclei crash together to form a nucleus of four protons and four neutrons. This is called a beryllium-8 nucleus. It is not the stable beryllium that we know on earth, which has another neutron and is called beryllium-9. Beryllium-8 is an unstable isotope that has a fantastically short life and flies apart almost as soon as it is formed—in less than a millionth of a millionth of a second. Only if another helium nucleus crashes into the unstable beryllium nucleus in the brief moment of its life do the parts remain together and form a new stable nucleus of six protons and six neutrons.

This is the moment when a carbon nucleus is truly born. The atom of carbon whose story we are telling was born by this extraordinary chance billions of years ago.

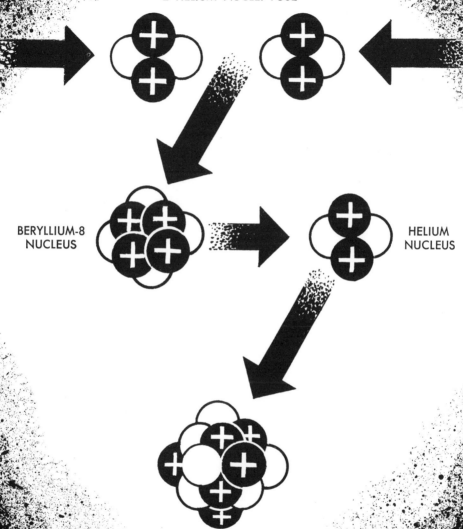

2 HELIUM NUCLEI FUSE

BERYLLIUM-8 NUCLEUS

HELIUM NUCLEUS

CARBON NUCLEUS

How, then, does the carbon atom get out of the star and come here to earth? The aging star goes on building up carbon atoms and other heavier atoms from its helium. Finally these nuclear reactions stop. The star collapses, the temperature rises suddenly, and the star explodes, scattering the carbon and other atoms through space. There they become mixed with the dust and thin sea of hydrogen gas which fill space.

THE "CRAB" NEBULA IS THE REMAINS
OF AN EXPLOSION OF A GIANT STAR

Mount Wilson and Palomar Observatories

THE ORION NEBULA
IS A CLOUD OF GAS
IN WHICH NEW
STARS ARE FORMING

Mount Wilson and Palomar Observatories

Later when a fresh star begins to form from this hydrogen gas and dust, it catches up some of the carbon and other atoms with it. There are fresh stars being formed like this all the time, and one of these fresh stars is the sun, which was formed four or five billion years ago.

ELEMENTS ARE BUILT IN STARS

STAR MATERIAL
EXPLODES
INTO SPACE

THE MATERIAL
IS MIXED WITH
THE DUST AND
GAS IN SPACE

NEW STARS ARE
FORMED FROM
THE DUST AND
GAS CLOUDS

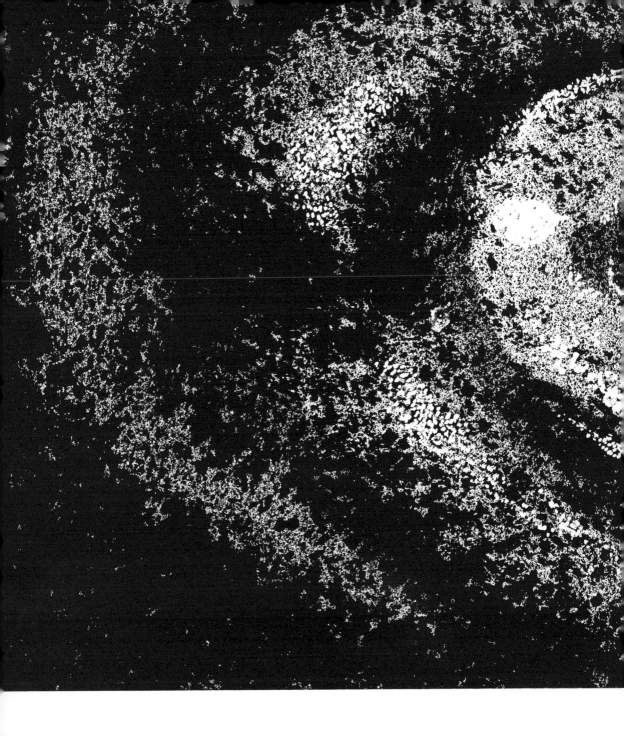

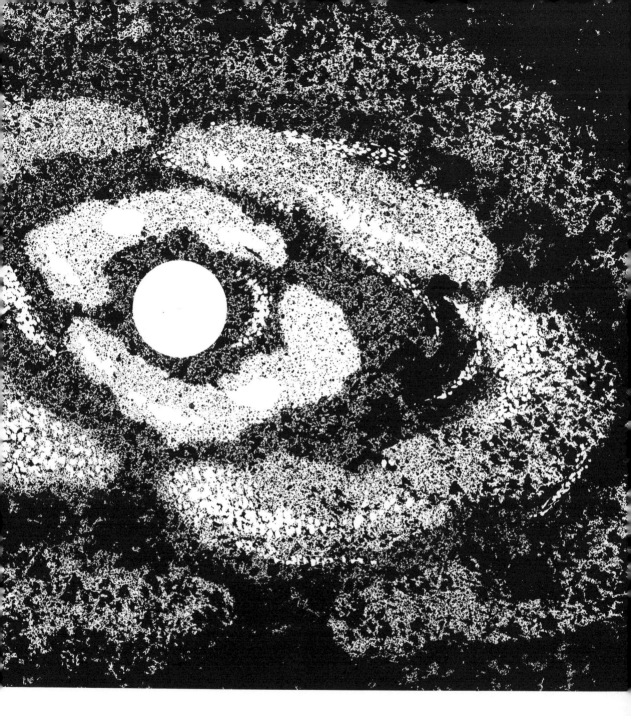

Later the earth and the other planets were formed from the sun.
The carbon atom was part of the earth when it was formed.

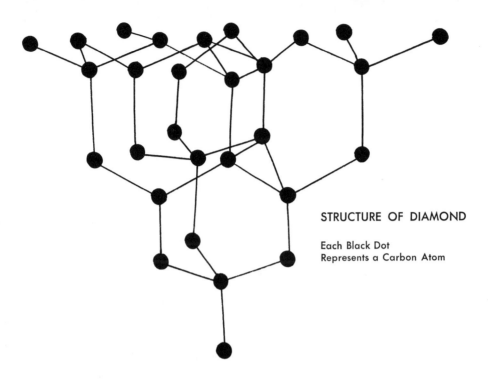

STRUCTURE OF DIAMOND

Each Black Dot
Represents a Carbon Atom

The carbon atom has been part of many different things, dead and alive, since the earth began. It has joined with other atoms, broken away, and then joined other atoms again. But always it has remained the same carbon atom.

At one time the carbon atom may have been part of a diamond— a pure crystal of carbon.

Courtesy of the American Museum of Natural History

Or it may have joined with two atoms of oxygen to form the gas carbon dioxide. The carbon dioxide may have entered through the pores of a leaf and been used to make sugar when the sunlight struck it there. The sugar became part of the tissues of the plant.

34

17520

That plant may have become peat or coal. When the plant died and fell to the ground, bacteria broke some of it down into simpler chemical substances—ammonia, water, and carbon dioxide. The carbon dioxide may have escaped into the air and been used again by other plants. But most of the carbon in the plant tissue remained in the ground. With other dead plants around it, the plant got pressed down by layers of sand, mud, and water that settled on it. Over millions of years the plants changed and hardened until they became hard coal, deep in the ground.

COAL LAYER

Courtesy of the American Museum of Natural History

The carbon atom may have been locked in the coal for millions of years. But one day it was dug out of the earth. When the coal was burned, the carbon atom joined with oxygen again and formed carbon dioxide. The next time it entered through the pores of a leaf into a plant, it was used again to make sugar. The plant was perhaps eaten by a cow. One of your forefathers may have drunk the milk of that cow or eaten a steak from it, and the carbon atom might have been in either.

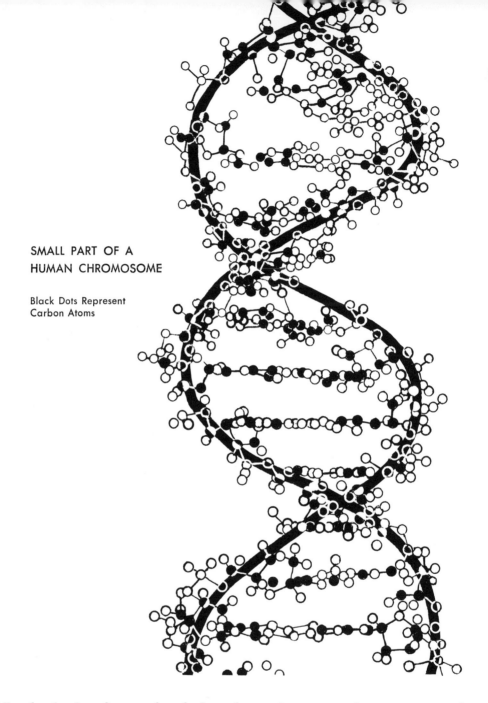

SMALL PART OF A
HUMAN CHROMOSOME

Black Dots Represent
Carbon Atoms

In the body of your forefather the carbon atom became part of one of the chromosomes which was passed on to your parents and then to you.

You may pass this carbon atom to a son or daughter. Or perhaps you will die with this carbon atom still in your body. But the career of the carbon atom is not over. It will return to the soil and from there it may get into the air again as carbon dioxide and pass in and out of the lungs of human beings for thousands of years.

The air in a man's lungs at any moment contains 10,000,000,-000,000,000,000,000 atoms, so sooner or later every one of us breathes an atom that has been breathed by someone who has lived before us—perhaps Michelangelo or George Washington or Moses! Your carbon atom, linked with atoms of oxygen, may be breathed by some great man or woman of the future. Then it may return again to the soil and lie dormant in some mineral for millions of years. And in time its cycle of life may begin again.

Will this cycle ever end? We do not know. Your carbon atom has been unchanged, as an atom, for four billion years or more, and there is no reason why it should not go on forever. Even if the earth is burned up at last by the sun, your carbon atom may go back into space and be swept again into some new star.

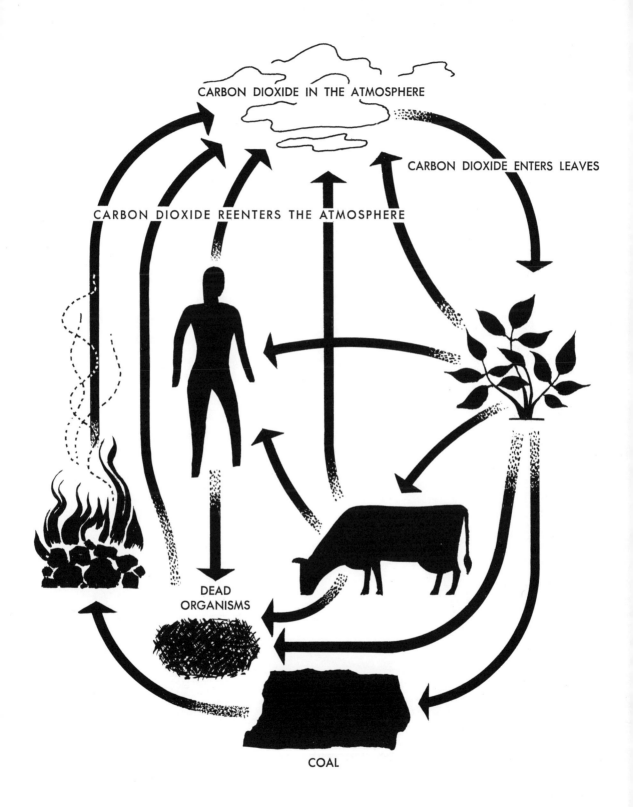

CARBON DIOXIDE IN THE ATMOSPHERE

CARBON DIOXIDE ENTERS LEAVES

CARBON DIOXIDE REENTERS THE ATMOSPHERE

DEAD ORGANISMS

COAL

In a star, and only in a star, will its identity finally disappear. It will be broken apart by violent atomic collisions and its pieces built into other atoms. Then, and only then, will the career of your carbon atom be at an end. But it will be part of new atoms of a different kind. And in this sense it will go on forever—a never-ending link between you and the stars.

SECTION OF THE MILKY WAY

Mount Wilson and Palomar Observatories

DR. J. BRONOWSKI is the distinguished author of such noted adult books as SCIENCE AND HUMAN VALUES and THE WESTERN INTELLECTUAL TRADITION. Educated at Cambridge University in England, Dr. Bronowski has been a Head of Projects for UNESCO, a Carnegie Visiting Professor at the Massachusetts Institute of Technology, and is a Foreign Honorary Member of the American Academy of Arts and Sciences. At present he is engaged in research at the Salk Institute for Biological Studies, in California.

MILLICENT E. SELSAM, a native New Yorker, majored in biology at Brooklyn College, took her M.A. in botany at Columbia University, and has taught biology on both the high school and college levels. Her writing has received wide acclaim for its scientific accuracy and simple presentation. Mrs. Selsam is a member of the Board of Directors of the American Nature Study Society and a Fellow of the American Association for the Advancement of Science.

WEIMER PURSELL studied at the Art Institute and the New Bauhaus School of Design in Chicago. Except for five years of college teaching, his whole career has been devoted to free-lance work in design and illustration.

Format by Kohar Alexanian
Set in Linotype Times Roman
Composed by Boro Typographers, Inc.
Printed by The Murray Printing Co.
Bound by American Book-Stratford Press
HARPER & ROW, PUBLISHERS, INCORPORATED

Date Due

JE 30 '69			
JE 6 '70			
FE 28 '74			
FE 21 '77			
JE 16 '80			
AG 8 '80			
MY 4 '81			
MR 19 '82			
JE 10 '82			